Caretta
the Top Turtle

Library of Congress Control Number: 2007905894
SAN: 257-6295

Publisher's Cataloging-in-Publication
(Provided by Quality Books, Inc.)

Glenn, Gloria.
Caretta : the top turtle / by Gloria Glenn; illustrated by Joanna Ritchie Britt and John Moises Webb.
p. cm.
SUMMARY: Chronicle of the life of a loggerhead sea turtle, from the egg to nesting on her home beach.
Audience: Ages 8-12.
ISBN-13: 978-0-9774698-0-2
ISBN-10: 0-9774698-0-8

1. Loggerhead turtle--Life cycles--Juvenile literature. [1. Loggerhead turtle. 3. Turtles.] I. Britt, Joanna Ritchie. II. Webb, John Moises. III. Title.

QL666.C536G54 2007 597.92 QBI07-700137

www.ggtoptrtle.com

106 Carr Court, Mebane NC 27302, or call 919-563-0677

Published in the United States of America.
Cover and interior design by Sandi Welch/2W Design Group, llc.

# Caretta

## the Top Turtle

*by* Gloria Glenn

*illustrated by* Joanna Ritchie Britt
*and* John Moises Webb

*Mebane, NC*

*To Les, Terry, and Lisa, my children*
*in the order of their appearance*
*and to Becky,*
*who loved Caretta*

# Acknowledgments

My thanks to Orville Clayton, who introduced me to baby Caretta, and toVirginia Sanders and the other members of the Longboat Key Turtle Watch Patrol, who engendered in me a reverence for this majestic creature of the sea. Thanks to Matthew Godfrey, Project Biologist, North Carolina Wildlife Resources Commission, for editing Caretta's story and bringing me up-to-date on sea turtle facts. And many thanks to Nita Wrenn for her invaluable help. I am also grateful to Adam Eisenson, Kristin Bedell, and Carlene Morton for advice and support.

# Table of Contents

# CHAPTER ONE

## The Hatchlings

About an arm's-length under the sand of a southern beach, Caretta, the baby loggerhead turtle, strains against her shell. She has been inside for a long time—almost two months—and now she struggles to be free.

She doesn't know why she wants to get out, only that she feels so very cramped. Curled inside her special sac, her nose almost touches her tiny tail and flippers. The sac, once a comfortable bed, grows tighter each day.

She tosses her head back and forth, trying to find more room. A sharp spine, called an egg tooth, on the end of her nose cuts through the sac, now pressing against the shell.

The yolk of her egg still clings to her abdomen, feeding her. As Caretta grows bigger, her yolk shrinks.

Time after time, her egg tooth bumps the eggshell until it breaks open. Finally, the little loggerhead pushes a hole through the white shell. Some egg white runs onto the sand. She pokes her head out, then her front flippers, and . . .

She has to rest.

Sand sifts on top of her and beside her. She feels other eggs around her. They are the same as the one she has broken through—round, rubbery, the size of a ping pong ball.

She rests for almost two days, half in and half out of her shell. At last she struggles all the way out.

Now she has some space. But that space continually changes.

Sometimes the sand in her nest feels warm and sometimes it feels cool.

Caretta is the top turtle. She likes the cool sand best. That's when she moves about more.

The egg next to her begins to break open. Wider and wider the crack grows until another head exactly like hers forces its way out. Soon a sister turtle crawls into the nest cavity.

As the two loggerheads explore the nest, other eggs split apart. Many brothers and sisters push out.

They crawl over each other, with long front flippers nudging each neighbor's dark brown carapace (the top shell) to make room. They stretch and rest amid the clutter of empty eggshells.

A short distance down the beach, a mother raccoon steals from the scrub oaks with her family one night. She smells the eggs in a fresh turtle nest and digs them up. The raccoons have a feast on the eggs.

How lucky that the raccoons didn't find Caretta's nest!

The little turtle has no way of understanding that the night air makes the temperature of the sand drop. All she knows is that she feels like flailing her flippers about when that delicious coolness comes. Sand her mother has packed down over the clutch of eggs loosens and lands beneath her feet, lifting her closer to the surface of the ground.

The other babies wave their flippers, too, clawing more sand onto the nest floor. Gradually, more than one hundred hatchlings are lifted upward, with Caretta still on top.

What a scratching as the hatchlings work their way higher and higher!

The next morning the sun warms the sand above the top turtle, and she stops moving. Her brothers and sisters stop, too.

Everybody is quiet until sunset.

The approaching dark takes away the heat in the final thin layer of sand above the hatchlings. Caretta again pushes up toward the surface of the sand. Her brothers and sisters follow, scrambling over each other in their hurry to reach the top.

With one swipe of her flipper, she flings aside the last bit of sand and bursts out into the night air. A scraping noise comes from the ground. Like bursting bubbles in a pot of oatmeal, the sand is astir with infant turtles popping out.

A mist over the nest turns into a light drizzle. Caretta sees a faint shine where water meets the eastern sky and heads that way.

# CHAPTER TWO

A vast world lies before Caretta—bigger than she has ever imagined. Palmetto leaves rustle like paper in the wind. A wide beach stretches as far as she can see.

No parent turtle has shown her what to do. Somewhere deep inside her, a memory stirs. It is a memory of some unspoken message that her ancestors have received for millions of years: "Move away from the shadows. Go quickly!"

And that same message tells her to memorize the beach, for one day—she does not know when—she will return to this place.

Without a look behind her, she fixes her elderberry-sized eyes on the horizon. Once again she sets her limbs in motion. What a sight! Leading an army of two-inch loggerheads, Caretta marches double-time over the sand, past the sea oats and ghost crab holes, toward the glistening sea.

Something suddenly grabs Caretta. She tumbles head over flipper, fighting madly to wrench herself free.

Ouch! Her attacker twists her right front flipper and snaps his pincer at her neck.

It's a ghost crab, white and frightening against the gray sky.

The crab does not have a firm grip on Caretta's flipper. She manages to jerk herself out of its clutches. The crab's claw lashes out at her again. She dodges the creature and takes off running.

She's headed the wrong way!

Standing on the tips of its eight pointed legs, the crab scoots after her.

The ghost crab scurries much faster than Caretta. But another nest mate gets in the way, and the crab catches him instead.

The crab drags him off to its burrow. Other ghost crabs, looking for a fast meal, pounce on the baby loggerheads. Snap, snap! One by one the poor babies disappear into the round crab tunnels.

Caretta does not waste much time deciding which way to go. She turns again toward the pale glimmer on the ocean. As she races to the sea, her flippers leave a trail of tracks like miniature tractor treads.

A wadded-up napkin sprawls across her path. She steps over it and falls headlong into a paper cup someone has tossed onto the beach. She could get away, except that the cup is caught in the trash. And besides, she doesn't know how to crawl backwards. She pushes as hard as she can. She tries again, but it's no use.

She is hopelessly trapped! Another hatchling accidentally shoves against the side of Caretta's cup prison. The cup rolls over and she tumbles out.

She's . . . out . . . of . . . breath, but she soon gets her second wind and races toward the water.

She reaches the edge of the surf where a wave has slipped back into the ocean. Pressing on through the crooked line of salty bubbles on the beach, she knows this is the place where she is supposed to be.

She paddles through the first waves flowing onto the shore. The next wave rumbles in, threatening to throw her back onto the beach. She dives underneath and rides the undertow out to sea. Her flippers no longer touch bottom. She paddles furiously, past the breakers and into quieter water. Pausing a few moments, she rocks in her cradle of swells. Here and there the raindrops splash into the ocean.

Caretta begins to swim again, farther and farther away from land. A big grouper tries to catch her. She scrambles aboard a piece of driftwood.

Safe at last!

Thirty years will pass before she is to see her home beach again.

# CHAPTER THREE

Rain gives way to a steady offshore wind. The Atlantic Ocean becomes deeper. Stars in the night sky lead Caretta eastward through the sparkles on the ever-tossing sea. Magnetic particles inside her head help her memorize where she has been.

In a frenzy to reach the open sea, she paddles with her brothers and sisters for two days. At last she finds a driftline, where two currents come together. A patch of floating seaweed and debris called flotsam swirls in the currents. She manages to crawl aboard. Exhausted, she nibbles a seaweed leaf—her first nourishment outside the nest—and sleeps with her front flippers folded back over the edge of her carapace.

Out of one hundred and thirty-nine hatchlings from the same nest, only eighty-one are left. They will face many more dangers in the next seventy-five or more years of their lives. But if people do not interfere, the dangers will grow less as they reach maturity.

Caretta awakes as a gray sky replaces the black of night, turning the ocean to shades of light and dark silver. Red and yellow streaks flame on the horizon and spill out into a path on the water.

She swims and rests, swims and rests. The gleaming water gradually loses its greenish color and becomes bluer. She clambers onto a clump of brown sargassum and lies still for a long, long time.

When Caretta opens her eyes, she sees baby turtles, their dark shells shining with moisture from the sea, on other patches of algae. Two more turtles climb onto her floating island. All three poke their heads between the branches, exploring their resting place.

Caretta's yolk is used up. She feels empty. She looks for something to eat. A tiny plankton animal swims by. Its body waves and slithers right under her nose. She eyes the animal, snaps at her prey, and misses. She tries again, catches it, and gobbles it up. She has never known anything could taste so sweet; but more would suit her better.

A piece of seaweed drifts by. A baby spiny lobster swims onto a green leaf and pauses. Caretta gobbles that up, too. Now she is getting the hang of this eating business. She swallows an infant snail and has a bite or two of algae.

As Caretta and the rest of the babies drift out to sea, they taste other things. One hatchling is very sick from eating a small lump of tar he found in the flotsam. He has also eaten a splinter of driftwood that Caretta herself almost ate.

Pleasantly full at last, Caretta again becomes still as warm swells from the Gulf Stream rock her raft. Far behind her, a flock of sea birds fly toward the driftline, circle the flotsam, and dive for sealife.

"Augh, augh!" The scream of a herring gull startles Caretta. The monstrous thing swoops down and carries off a baby turtle.

The gulls pick off first one and then another of her brothers and sisters.

Baby turtles slide under the algae and flotsam. Caretta, too, scurries under their floating mat. In a blur she sees one gull, then another, dive through the air, their fierce beaks barely missing her. They carry away more of her brothers and sisters.

Coming up occasionally for a breath of air, she hides under the sargassum branches until the cries of the gulls die away. Then she again climbs aboard her raft.

She will stay there as long as she can find food and a place to hide.

# CHAPTER FOUR

# The Sargasso Sea

Each day Caretta swims farther away from the driftline. One day she chases a little fish into the warm Gulf Stream. She wolfs down the fish and climbs aboard a string of seaweed.

She finds some leafhoppers on top. Caretta has never tasted insects before. They wiggle temptingly on the leaf. She must have a bite. It's easy. The first time she snaps at one, she catches it. Another good taste! She sees more insects. She eats a fly, an aphid, and a beetle.

Something moves in the water below her, probably more fish. Caretta eases to the edge of her perch and sticks her head under. A school of fish comes swimming by. They are exactly the right size to eat. She slips off her mat and goes after them.

Caretta is so busy chasing fish round and round the float that she doesn't see a big shape swimming toward her. Suddenly the long body of a tuna fish comes into view. Its mouth is open wide. It's heading straight for her!

Caretta manages to scramble into a tangle of sargassum. Her lighter-colored plastron (the bottom shell) affords a camouflage, making her difficult to see. The fish noses about for a few minutes and swims away. Long after the tuna has passed by, she lies motionless among the branches, afraid to venture out again.

She rides her newly found raft as it floats to the Sargasso Sea in the North Atlantic. There she is content to swim from one sargassum colony to the other, feeding on the little creatures that live among the brown leaves and plant bladders. She occasionally swallows a bladder or a tiny bit of plankton. She eats sargassum fish, baby sea horses, sea worms, snails, and fish eggs she finds on the leaves.

As she grows into a juvenile, her carapace turns reddish-brown with tinges of yellow on her body and limbs. She could fit in the palm of your hand at birth. At the end of her first year she was about the size of a dinner plate, and now she is becoming very large and heavy.

For ten years Caretta drifts with the ocean currents, foraging for all sorts of sea animals. She can swim much faster than a person. Now she spends a great deal of time in the islands off the coast of North Africa. In the Azores, she stalks a large crab, grabs it, and chomps on the shell until it opens. Then she samples the meat. It's delicious!

Caretta has no teeth, but her jaws become stronger each year. She is able to crush the hardest shellfish. On a reef near Madeira, she tastes gooseneck barnacles, acorn barnacles, and mollusks. Soft creatures are also a treat. In the Canary Islands she feasts on shrimp, anemones, and jellyfish. Now she knows she can find all kinds of good things to eat in the sea. She hardly ever eats plants any more.

In the North Atlantic she faces another danger: people! Some fishermen drop their baited long-line hooks into a soft coral reef. Caretta grabs the bait. A large fishhook pierces her mouth. How it hurts! That's the second time she has felt pain. She tosses her head back and forth, trying to rid herself of the hateful thing.

She can't get it out of her mouth.

The fishermen pull her into the boat. Her flippers wave in the air. Her heart beats wildly. As gently as they can, the men work the hook from her mouth. Then they lower Caretta back into the water. She painfully swims away with a stream of blood trailing behind her.

She does not feel like eating anything for a long time. When her mouth is not quite so sore, she eats only jellyfish and other soft foods.

Caretta's wounds heal at last. She is not an easy prey for predators any more. Her shell is tougher, and she can swim many miles every day to find the larger sea life she feeds on. She forages alone and rests under rocks and coral reefs, or on the ocean floor, holding her breath for longer periods of time.

# CHAPTER FIVE

## Fate, Freeze, and Forage

Caretta, once a tiny baby at the top of her nest, now weighs 200 pounds. She is more than half grown. Life in the ocean is usually safe for her. Except for man, her worst enemy is the shark. A huge shark chases her one day. Because she cannot pull her flippers and head into her shell like land turtles do, she scoots under a rock ledge and tucks her limbs close to her body. The shark circles the rock, searching for a way to get at her, then glides off, looking for easier prey.

Caretta once saw a shark attack a green turtle that didn't see the shark coming. The shark bit the unwary turtle's flipper. Though the turtle escaped, a part of its flipper was lost to the shark's greedy jaws.

One January day when Caretta is almost full-grown, she wanders into the Mosquito Lagoon near the Kennedy Space Center in Florida, hunting horseshoe crabs, one of her favorite foods. As she pauses for a time on the bottom of the lagoon after an especially big meal, the temperature of the water drops.

Stunned by the cold, her body settles in the soft mud. She is so very sleepy . . .

Caretta is freezing to death.

She wakes up in a comfortable place. Someone who discovered her in the lagoon keeps her in a warm pool and feeds her until the ocean temperature becomes high enough for her to survive. Then he releases Caretta into the ocean.

The next winter is cold, too, but not quite as cold as the one before. Caretta has been in the barge canal at Port Canaveral many times, and she seeks refuge there. On the way to the canal, she swims into a net dragged by shrimpers trolling nearby. Desperately she tries to claw her way out before she runs out of breath.

Ordinarily, a sea turtle would drown in a shrimper's net. However, these people have a TED (Turtle Excluder Device) built into theirs. Caretta escapes through a specially-designed trap door without tearing the net or being harmed herself. She is free again, free to surface for a breath of fresh air.

During the winter, the barge canal is a busy place. Dredges scoop up the mud on the bottom to make the canal deeper. The temperature drops dangerously low. Slowed down by the cold water, Caretta dodges a dredge, barely missing the sucking and grinding of the powerful machine. Finally she manages to make her way out of the canal, around the jetties, into the sea, and to a warmer place farther south.

When Caretta recovers, she is ready to eat. Floating on the swells are the most beautiful things she has seen in a long time: a flotilla of Portuguese men-of-war. Huge jellyfish with purple sails!

She charges at her target. Clamping her strong jaws onto the first sail, she gives her great head a shake and tears off a chunk of jellyfish. She wolfs it down. Closing her eyes and pushing aside the stinging polyps, she snaps at another jellyfish. She continues to eat until her eyes are red and swollen from their stings. But she doesn't care. Drunk with hunger, she eats until she cannot hold another bite.

Other loggerheads come to gorge themselves until they, too, have red and swollen eyes. One turtle swallows a discarded plastic bag, thinking it's a jellyfish, and chokes to death.

Caretta has learned to care for herself to maturity. Throughout the years she visits many parts of the ocean to feed. Though predators still threaten her as she forages on coral reefs, in rivers, canals, and lagoons, she has learned to stay out of harm's way.

## CHAPTER SIX

# Moonlight Crawl

Caretta now weighs 350 pounds. Her carapace measures 36 inches from front to back. Using her sense of smell in the water flows of the ocean and the magnetic particles in her brain, she follows the Gulf Stream back to her birthplace. And only a short distance offshore, a male loggerhead is ready to mate with her.

Just beyond the breakers, he courts Caretta by nuzzling her head and gently nipping her neck and flippers. She is ready. He embraces her with his front claws hooked onto her carapace and curls his long tail under her during the mating. When the eggs are fertilized and the nesting process complete, neither parent will ever see the babies.

Later, full of fertilized eggs, Caretta heads for her home beach. A full moon casts a silver path on the water. Paddling past the swells and using her back flippers for a rudder, she easily propels herself through the breakers and onto the shore. It is the first time she has been on land since she left the nest thirty years ago. She is the only turtle in her nest to survive the dangers of the sea.

She slows somewhat as she crawls through the bubbling foam that disappears after each wave. Without the buoyancy of the water, she feels the weight of her body dragging over the sand. Each step becomes dryer and more difficult, but the eggs press against her, and the ancient memories tell her she must push on.

After pausing to rest, breathe, and choose her nesting place, Caretta crawls toward the dunes, plowing a pattern in the sand like tractor marks. At the foot of the dunes, she noses the ground. Finding the sand soft and dry enough, she clears away the plant debris.

Suddenly Caretta sees flashing lights and hears unfamiliar sounds.

Voices.

She lifts her giant head. Frightened, she turns to flee. Closer and closer the lights and voices come. Weary after her struggle over land, she hauls herself back toward the ocean. The lights follow. Voices ring out in all directions. The dangerous creatures—people—never touch Caretta, but she keeps on going until she is safe beyond the breakers.

She has made a false crawl.

Caretta waits offshore, eggs heavy inside her. She must get on land. If she has to make too many passes at the beach, she will be forced to void her eggs in the water.

The moon drops low in the sky. Eventually, Caretta sees no motion on land, nor does she hear any sound save the heaving of the sea. Choosing a spot close to her home beach, she again approaches the edge. From far away, a family of four people watches her swim toward shore.

All clear. Again she drags her heavy body across the foam, over the wet sand, and onto a soft, dry place.

The family hangs back. Silently they continue to watch.

Caretta nudges the ground, breathes heavily, and digs a body pit with her back flippers. Then she lowers herself into the shallow hole. Though she never has nested before, she knows exactly what to do. She cups her back flippers like hands and throws sand behind her, one flipperful at a time. At last she has scooped out a deeper hole shaped like a flask.

Sighing heavily, Caretta places her ovipositor over the hole and pushes out the first egg.

The family gathers around her and watches, speaking only in whispers.

Relief floods over Caretta as she squeezes out two more eggs, then another and another. Sticky tears run down her face, pressing out the sand and salt in her eyes and keeping them moist in the night air. Each time she forces out another egg or two, she raises her limbs for greater muscular strength.

About an hour or so after she first struggled across the sand, she lays a clutch of 120 eggs, as rubbery and white as the one she hatched out of so many years before. The only task left is to cover the nest and return to the sea.

Still using her back flippers, Caretta takes her time filling in the nest cavity. She packs the sand down with the weight of her body, then tries to make the disturbed area look as nearly as possible like the rest of the beach. Turning in circles, she uses all four flippers to fling sand over the place where she has dug. Lastly, her wearisome task complete, she swings her massive head toward the ocean. Plodding across the sand and into the surf, she leaves a horseshoe-shaped trail behind her.

At the edge of the water, sand clings to Caretta's shell. One of the people rubs some off. And as she returns to her home in the wild sea, the plankton in that sand glows red and green in the moonlight.

# Sea Turtle Facts

**THERE ARE SEVEN MAIN SPECIES OF SEA TURTLES:**

**Leatherback *(Dermochelys coriacea).*** The largest of the sea turtles. The largest leatherback recorded was a male weighing 2,000 pounds that was found dead on a Wales, UK, beach. The only sea turtle with a flexible shell. A mature leatherback is longer than a full-sized bicycle. Has no scutes. Backward-pointing spines in throat to help it swallow the jellyfish it eats. Can dive more than half a mile into the ocean depths. Body fat and a special heating system from heart to flippers enable the leatherback to live in extremely cold water. Regularly nest on Florida beaches, also beaches in the Caribbean, South America, and West Africa. Habitat: All oceans of the world.

**Green turtle *(Chelonia mydas).*** 200-500 pounds. Heart-shaped carapace is four feet long. The carapace is not really green. The turtle's name comes from the color of its fat (calipee), which was used to make green turtle soup before the practice was outlawed. The only sea turtle that eats mainly vegetation as an adult. Its beak has serrated edges to trim the grass and algae it eats. Swims great distances at a time. Green turtles in the Atlantic nest heavily on beaches in the eastern United States, Ascension Island, Central America, South America, and West Africa. Some populations of the Pacific green turtle are called black sea turtles because of their darker shell.

**Loggerhead *(Caretta caretta).*** 200-350 pounds. Sailors observing the loggerhead at sea so named it because they said the turtle's massive head looked like a log. A mature Caretta's shell is about 36 inches from front to back--as far as you could reach if you were to stretch your arms to the sides. Some are known to grow as long as five feet and weigh 600 pounds. Can travel as much as 40 miles in a day. One of the most common sea turtles in the Atlantic Ocean. Habitat: subtropical and temperate seas all over the world.

**Hawksbill *(Eretmochelys imbricata).*** Usually under 200 pounds. Carapace about two feet long. One hawksbill once weighed in at 300 pounds. Has a small head with a hooked beak (like the beak of a hawk). In some parts of the world, its scutes are made into "tortoiseshell" jewelry. Favorite food: sponges. Found in all tropical waters, around coral reefs, and in shallow coastal waters. In the Atlantic it ranges as far north as Massachusetts; in the Pacific, as far south as Peru.

**Kemp's ridley *(Lepidochelys kempii).*** Weighs less than 100 pounds. Domed shell. The most endangered sea turtle. In Rancho Nuevo, Mexico, they nest so heavily that nesting season is called "arribadas," meaning "arrival." The arribada usually occurs during daylight hours. Also nests in small numbers on South Padre Island in Texas. Habitat: West Atlantic Ocean, usually in shallow coastal waters. Range from Central America to Nova Scotia, Canada. Has never been seen south of the equator.

**Olive ridley *(Lepidochelys olivacea).*** Weighs less than 100 pounds. Flat, heart-shaped shell 28 inches long. Among the smallest of the sea turtles. Sometimes lays eggs in arribadas. Habitat: Pacific, Atlantic, and Indian Oceans. Seldom seen where loggerheads are. In Brazil, Olive ridleys and loggerheads nest at the same time on the same beaches.

**Flatback *(Natator depressus).*** Also called Australian flatback. Average weight, 180 pounds. Flat shell about three feet long, curling up at the sides. Not much known about flatbacks. Although it is a small species of sea turtle, its eggs are the largest of all reptiles, and the hatchlings are bigger. The only species of sea turtle not on the international endangered list. Nest only in Australia.

Sea turtles can swim 20 miles an hour, about four times faster than humans. After emerging from their nests, males almost never come ashore, and females come ashore only to nest. On some Pacific beaches, male green turtles will bask in the sun. Sea turtles mate offshore one to two months before nesting. Most sea turtles nest at night. Except for the arribadas, which can occur at any time, some nest occasionally in daylight hours.

When the eggs are incubating, the temperature of the sand determines the sex of the turtle. The incubation temperature that produces an equal number of males and females is called the "pivotal temperature," which is about 85 degrees in the United States. Females are produced at warmer temperatures while males develop at cooler temperatures.

Although sea turtles lay large clutches of eggs several times each year, scientists believe that only one out of every 1,000 baby turtles live to become adults. People are among their worst predators. They eat their meat, calipee, and eggs, use their shells for jewelry, their oil for cosmetics, and they destroy their habitat with buildings and sea walls that are too close to the tide line. In many beach areas, shore lights confuse hatchlings, causing them to crawl away from the ocean and across streets, where they are hit by cars or they die in the hot sun.

Turtle eggs make light cakes. But they're not good to fry, because the whites do not cook satisfactorily. In some countries, turtle eggs are believed to have mystical powers.

All sea turtle species are now on the United States endangered list. In the United States, it is against the law to harass, kill, or capture a sea turtle. If these laws are broken, the offender must pay a heavy fine or go to jail, or both.

The Atlantic coast of central Florida is the loggerhead sea turtles' second largest nesting place in the world; the first is Masirah Island in the Arabian Sea.

Because the ocean is so vast, tracking these sea giants is difficult. Some researchers have applied satellite tags on the shells of sea turtles to study their migrations. When the turtles come up to breathe, the signal is picked up by satellite and the information is recorded. Some phases of the turtles' lives are still unknown, such as how long it takes them to reach maturity and how long they live in the wild. Many researchers believe, for example, that the loggerhead can live 100 years. One thing is certain: giant sea turtles have lived in the oceans for millions of years. If people will leave them alone, they will be on this earth for many more.

# Glossary

**Beak**—the hooked end of a hawksbill turtle's mouth

**Bladder**—a bulb on the sargassum alga that traps air and helps it to float

**Boil**—When all the hatchlings in a nest emerge at once.

**Calipee**—the green sea turtle's fatty cartilage that's used in turtle soup

**Carapace**—a turtle's top shell

**Clutch**—a nest of eggs

**Crawl**—When a sea turtle comes up on the beach to lay her eggs, it's called a "crawl."

**Debris**—junk that collects on the ocean or on the beach

**Driftline**—a place where two ocean currents meet

**Environment**—one's surroundings

**Endangered Species act**—a law passed by Congress in 1973 to protect an animal or plant that's threatened with extinction. Anyone who hunts, collects, or engages in other harmful activities of an endangered or threatened species faces a fine or imprisonment, or both.

**Extinct**—no longer lives on the earth

**Flotilla**—a group of jellyfish floating near each other

**Flotsam**—floating seaweed and debris

**Forage**—to hunt for food

**Grouper**—a large saltwater fish

**Gulf stream**—a warm ocean current flowing from the Gulf of Mexico northward up the east coast of the United States to Nantucket, Massachusetts, and eastward into the North Atlantic Ocean

**Habitat**—the place where a plant or animal lives and gets food and shelter

**Hatchling**—a newly-hatched turtle

**Incubation**—Development of the turtle from the time its egg is deposited in the nest until it hatches, usually about 60 days

**Jetties**—a wall of rocks going from a canal or river a short distance into the sea to control the current

**Lagoon**—a shallow sound, channel, or pond connecting with a larger body of water

**Ovipositor**—the special part between the turtle's back shells that squeezes out eggs into the nest

**Pincer**—a crab's claw

**Plankton**—microscopic sea life

**Plastron**—a turtle's bottom shell

**Polyps**—the stinging parts of a man-of-war's tentacles

**Predators**—creatures that hunt and eat others

**Rudder**—a steering device

**Sac**—the membrane that forms a pouch inside the turtle's egg

**Sargasso Sea**—a sea in the middle of the North Atlantic where sargassum algae grow

**Scutes**—the hard plates that make up a sea turtle's carapace

**Swells**—the gentle waves beyond the breakers

**Species**—a biological rank

**TED**—Turtle Excluder Device (sometimes called a Trawler Efficiency Device) - an attachment to a shrimper's net fitted with bars to guide a sea turtle or other large marine life up through a trap door and out of the net. The shrimp and smaller catch then collect in the bottom of the net.

# Notes

# About the Author

**Gloria Glenn,** teacher and journalist, was born in Jacksonville, Florida. She received a B.A. in English at Jacksonville University and an MA. in Special Education at Florida State University. She taught special education in Jacksonville and language arts on the Space Coast. Two of her favorite pastimes were watching shuttle launches at Cape Kennedy and observing sea turtles on the beach. She gave up teaching to do freelance writing for the Florida Today newspaper and has published short stories for children. She lives in Mebane, North Carolina, with Polly, her retired racing greyhound.

# About the Illustrators

**Joanna Ritchie Britt** (l) is an artist, teacher, and mother, not necessarily in that order. Her art is inspired by the North Carolina landscape and the wonders of her children. She lives in Winston-Salem with her husband and four children.

**John Moises Webb** (r) loves to draw and paint. He lives in Mebane, North Carolina, where he runs track and studies art at Orange High.